Alfred's Basic Piano Library

Merry Christmas!

Willard A. Palmer ◆ Morton Manus ◆ Amanda Vick Lethco

Level 3

This book may be used with Level 3 or 4th book of any method.

CONTENTS

FOREWORD

Students enjoy playing Christmas Carols every year, and they find this gives them even more pleasure when they can choose from arrangements that are neither too easy nor too hard. Teachers find that properly graded Christmas pieces provide ideal supplementary selection. They are highly motivating, and they afford opportunities to reinforce the concepts and principles that the students need most at their own grade level.

This book is written to fit precisely with Level 3 of ALFRED'S BASIC PIANO LIBRARY, and it can be successfully used with the corresponding level of any piano course. At this level the students are capable of playing some novel arrangements of their favorites, with sleigh-bell and chime effects, etc., and the pieces are excellent for public performance.

The pieces are arranged in a graded order, and each one has a DUET PART, playable at the same piano. Measures are numbered to make practicing the duets easier.

The authors wish the teacher, student and parents a MERRY CHRISTMAS, and hope you will enjoy the new and special arrangements of Christmas music found in this book!

Second Edition

Jingle Bells

Allegro

James Pierpont

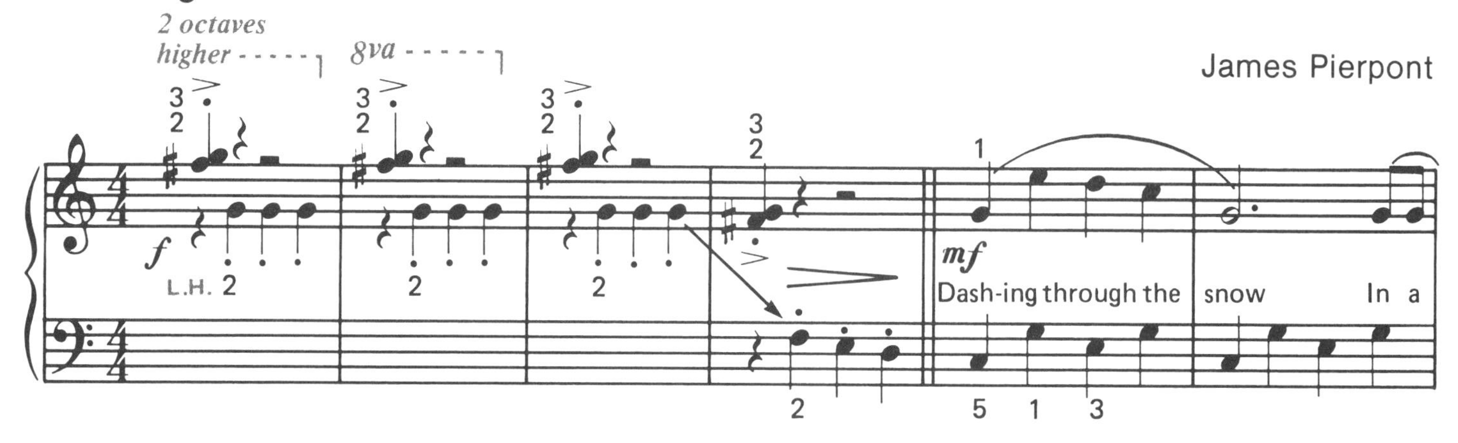

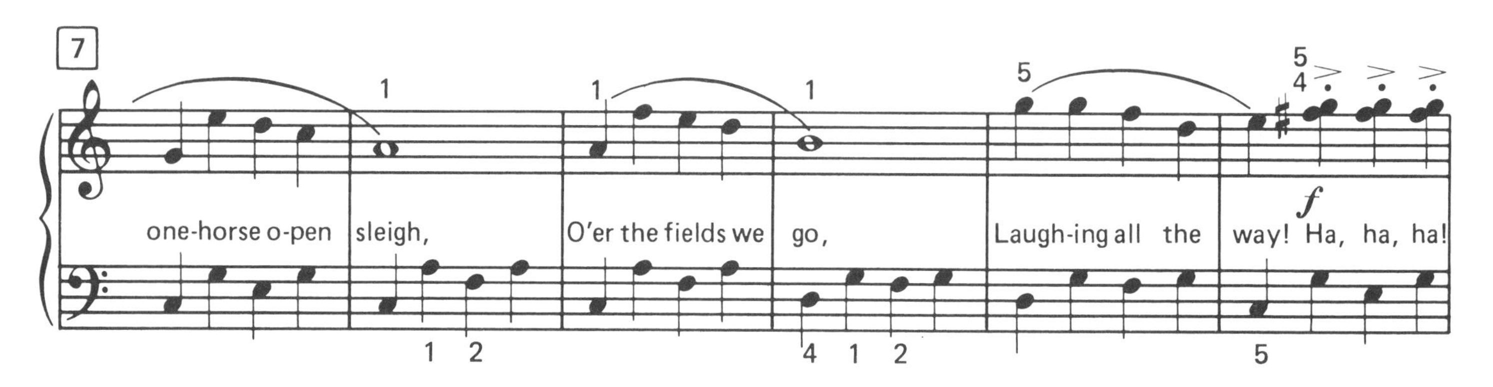

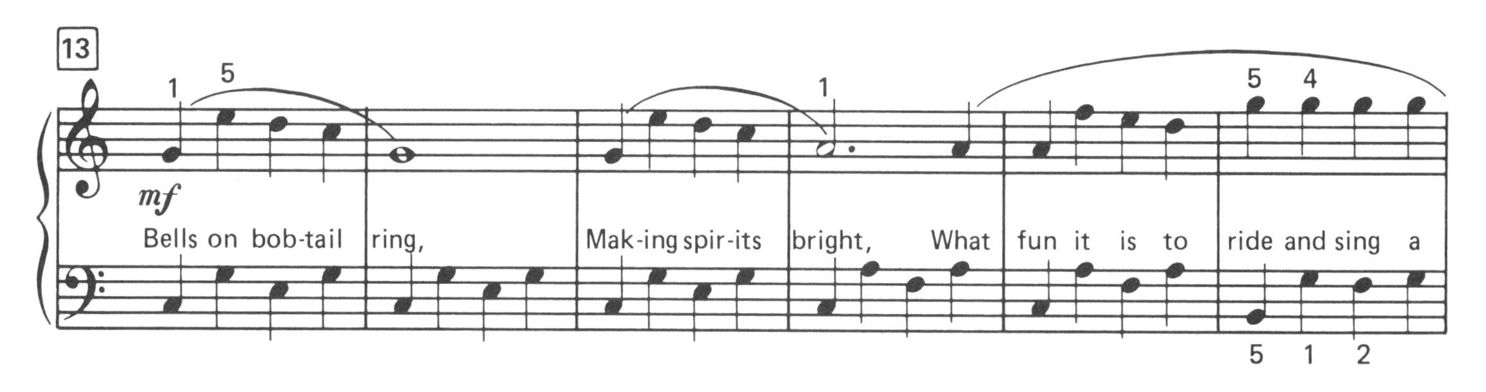

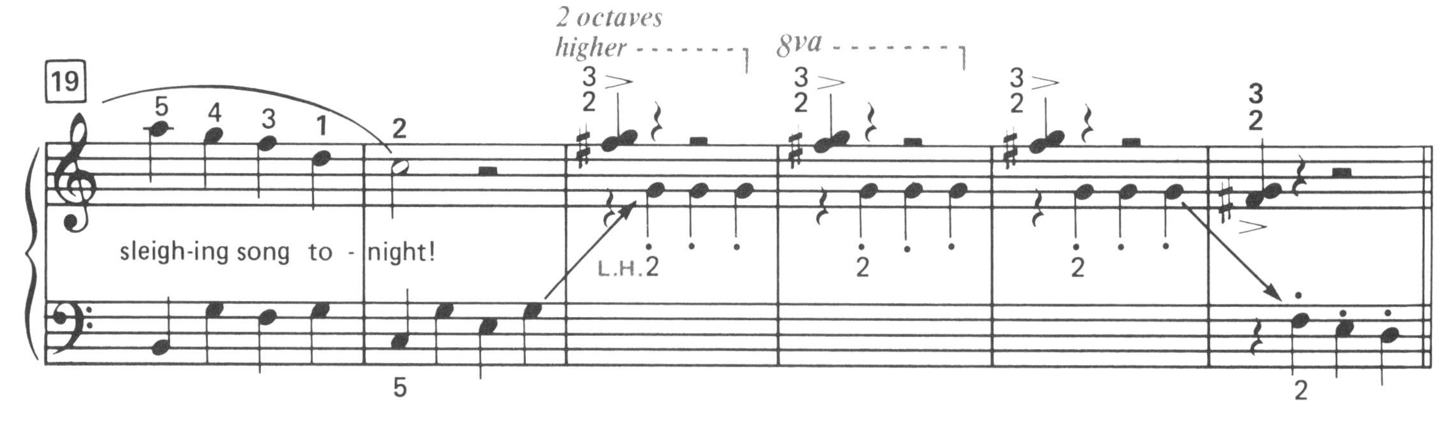

25
Jin-gle bells!
Jin-gle bells!
Jin-gle all the way!
Oh what fun it
30
1.
2.
is to ride in a one-horse o-pen sleigh! Ha, ha, ha!
one-horse o-pen sleigh!
35
8va
DUET PART:
Allegro
Play this part 8va throughout.
R.H.
L.H.
mf
(staccato)
7
13
19
25
30
1.
2.
35

We Wish You a Merry Christmas

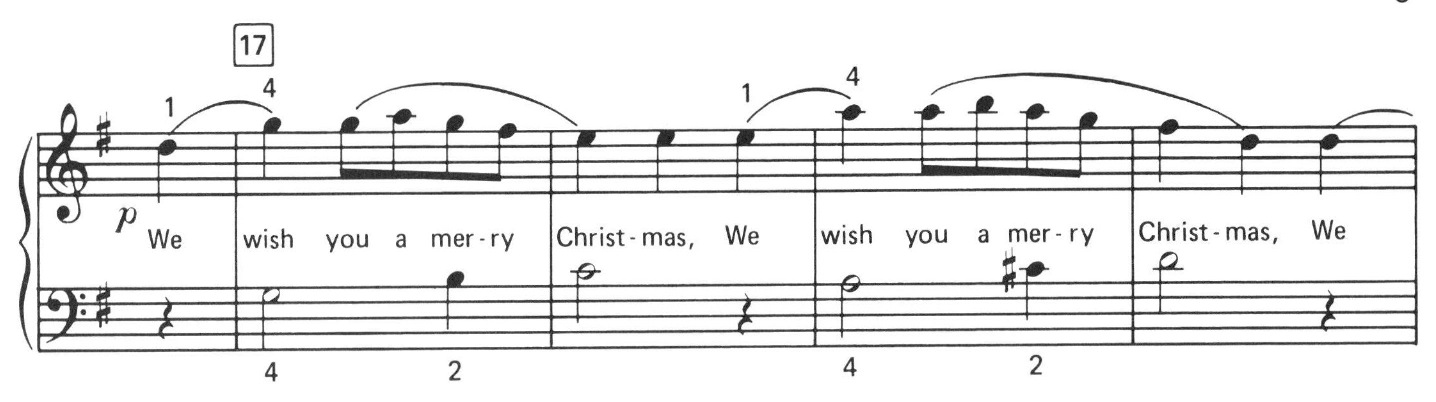
17
p
We wish you a mer-ry Christ-mas, We wish you a mer-ry Christ-mas, We

21
wish you a mer-ry Christ - mas, And a hap - py New Year!
ritardando

DUET PART:

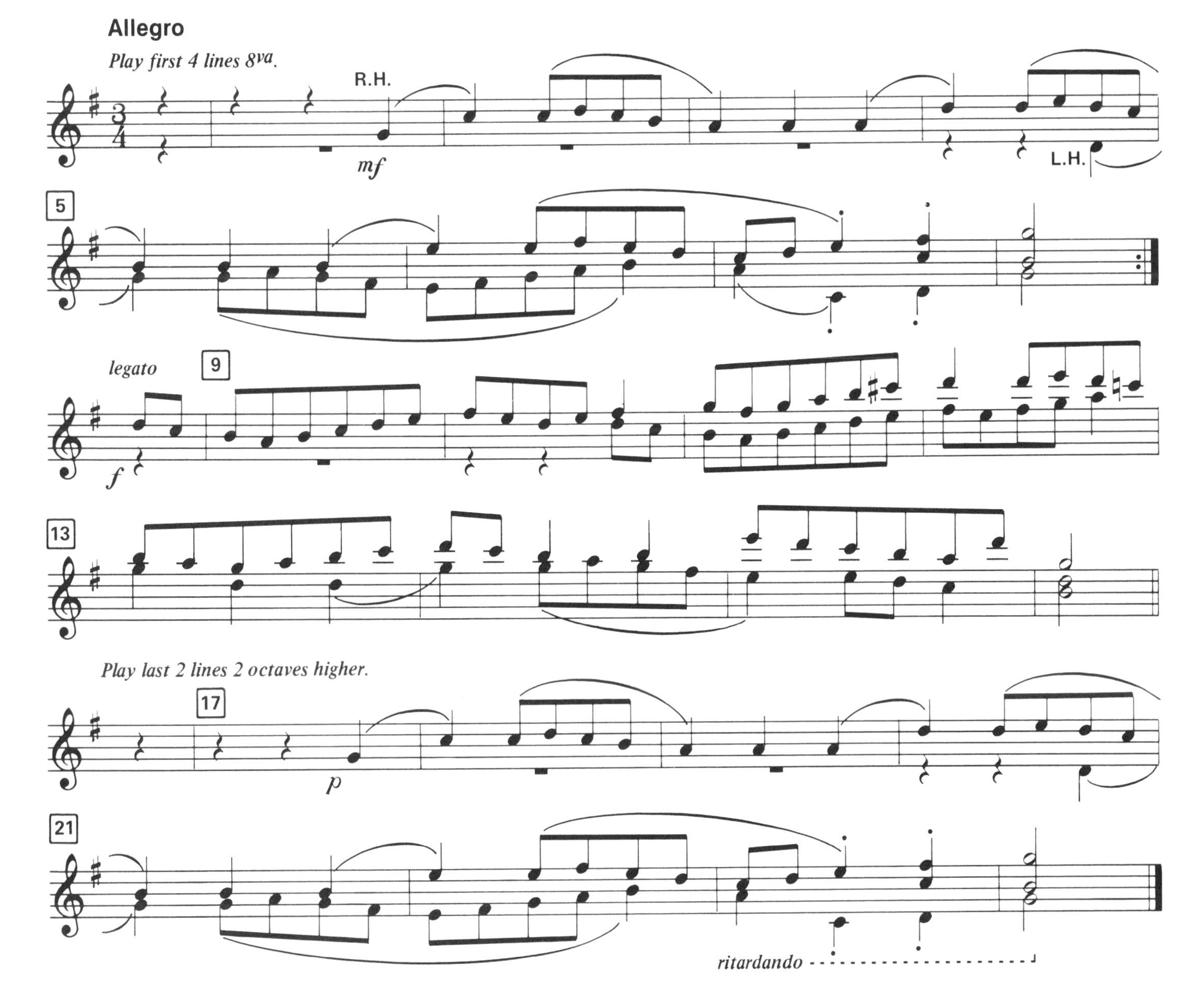
Allegro
Play first 4 lines 8va.
R.H.
mf
L.H.
5
legato
9
f
13
Play last 2 lines 2 octaves higher.
17
p
21
ritardando

Silent Night

*Measure 5—28 may be played as written if preferred, except when played as a duet.

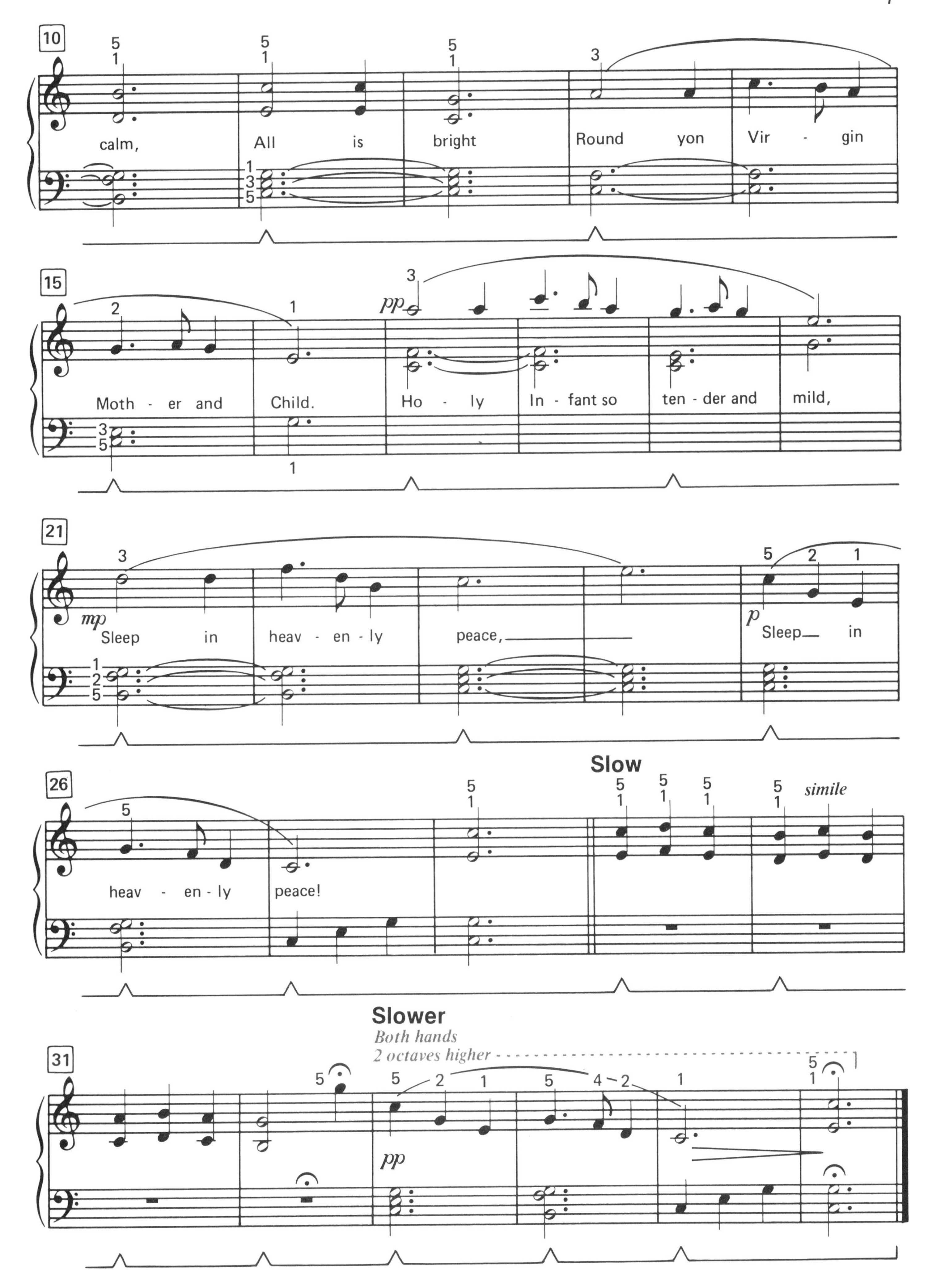
10
calm,
All is bright
Round yon Vir - gin
15
Moth - er and Child.
pp
Ho - ly In - fant so ten - der and mild,
21
mp
Sleep in heav - en - ly peace,
p
Sleep in
26
heav - en - ly peace!
Slow
simile
Slower
Both hands
2 octaves higher
31
pp

O Little Town of Bethlehem

Play all R.H. 6ths & 7ths with 1—5, except when marked otherwise.

DUET PART: (Student plays 1 octave higher.)

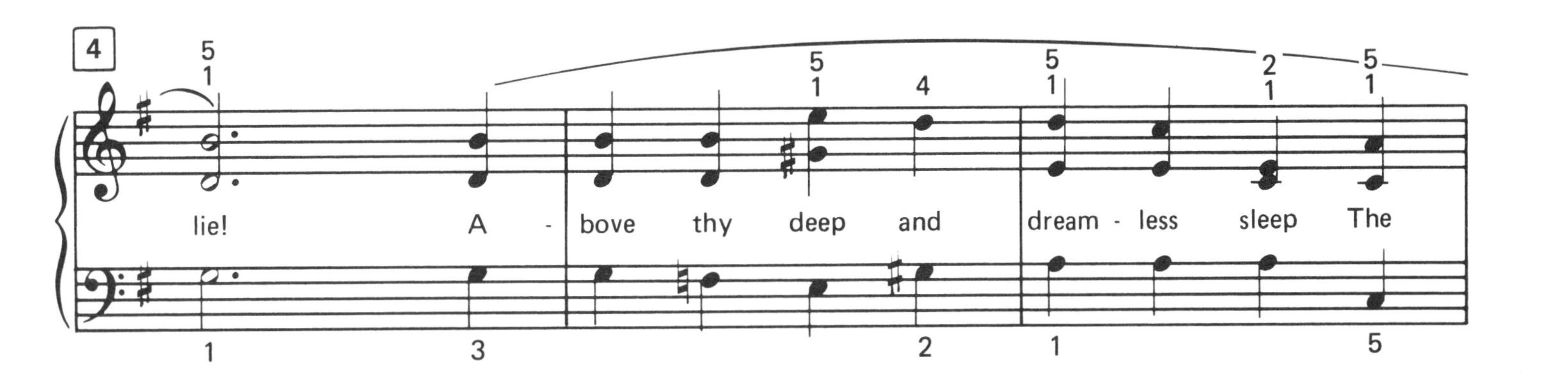
4
lie! A - bove thy deep and dream - less sleep The

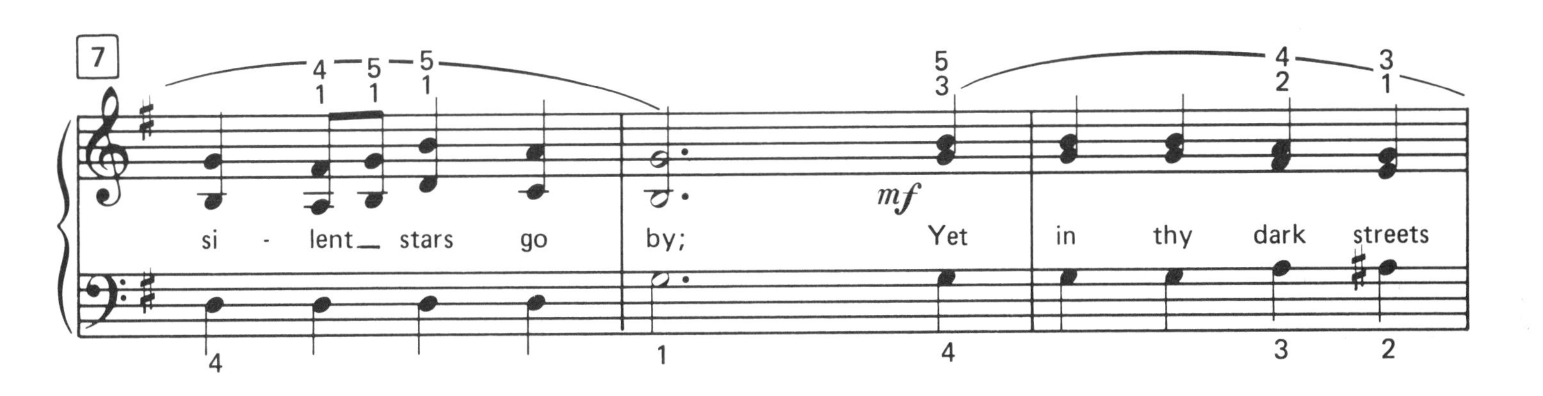
7
mf
si - lent stars go by; Yet in thy dark streets

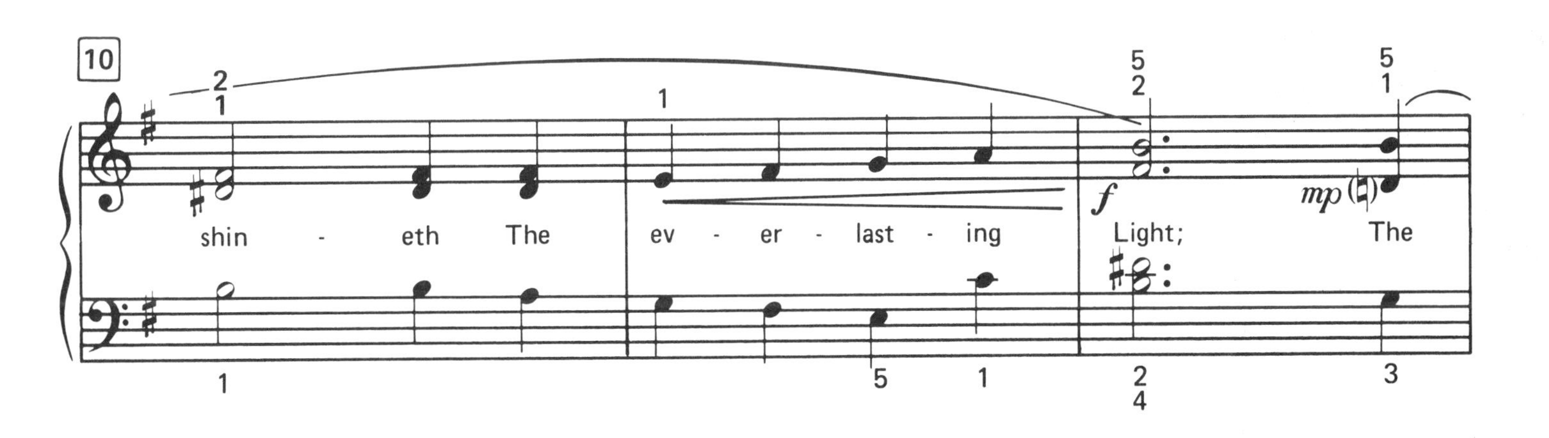
10
f
mp (♮)
shin - eth The ev - er - last - ing Light; The

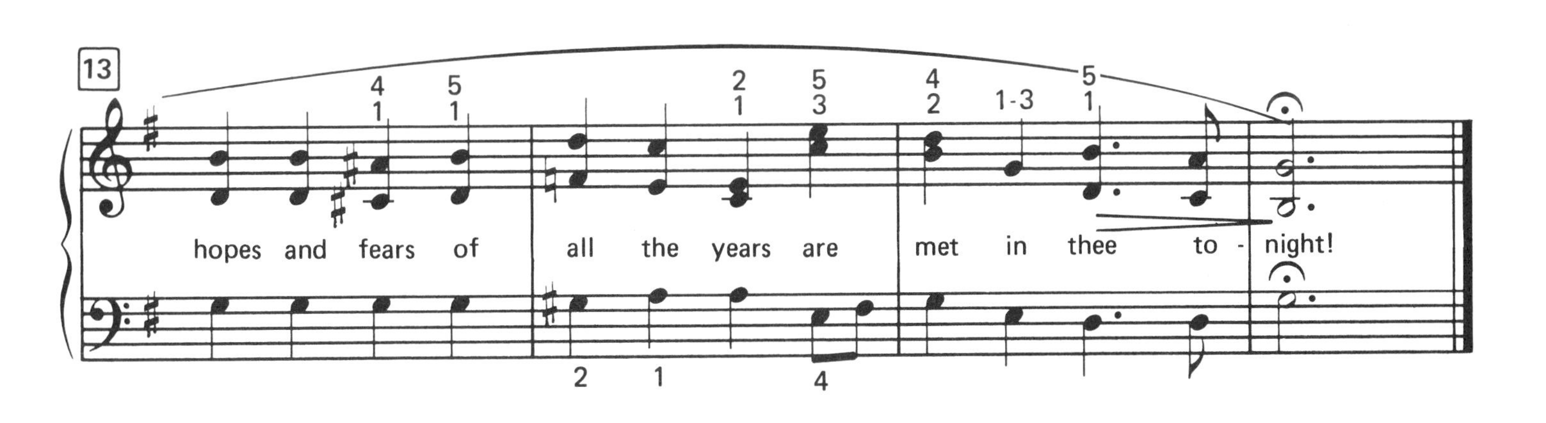
13
hopes and fears of all the years are met in thee to - night!

Over the River and Through the Woods

13
white and drift - ed snow.
17
O - ver the riv - er and through the woods, Oh,
21
how the wind does blow! It
25
stings the toes and bites the nose As
29
o - ver the ground we go!
L.H. over R.H.

Go Tell It on the Mountain

*Eighth notes should be played with a lilt, in long-short pairs!

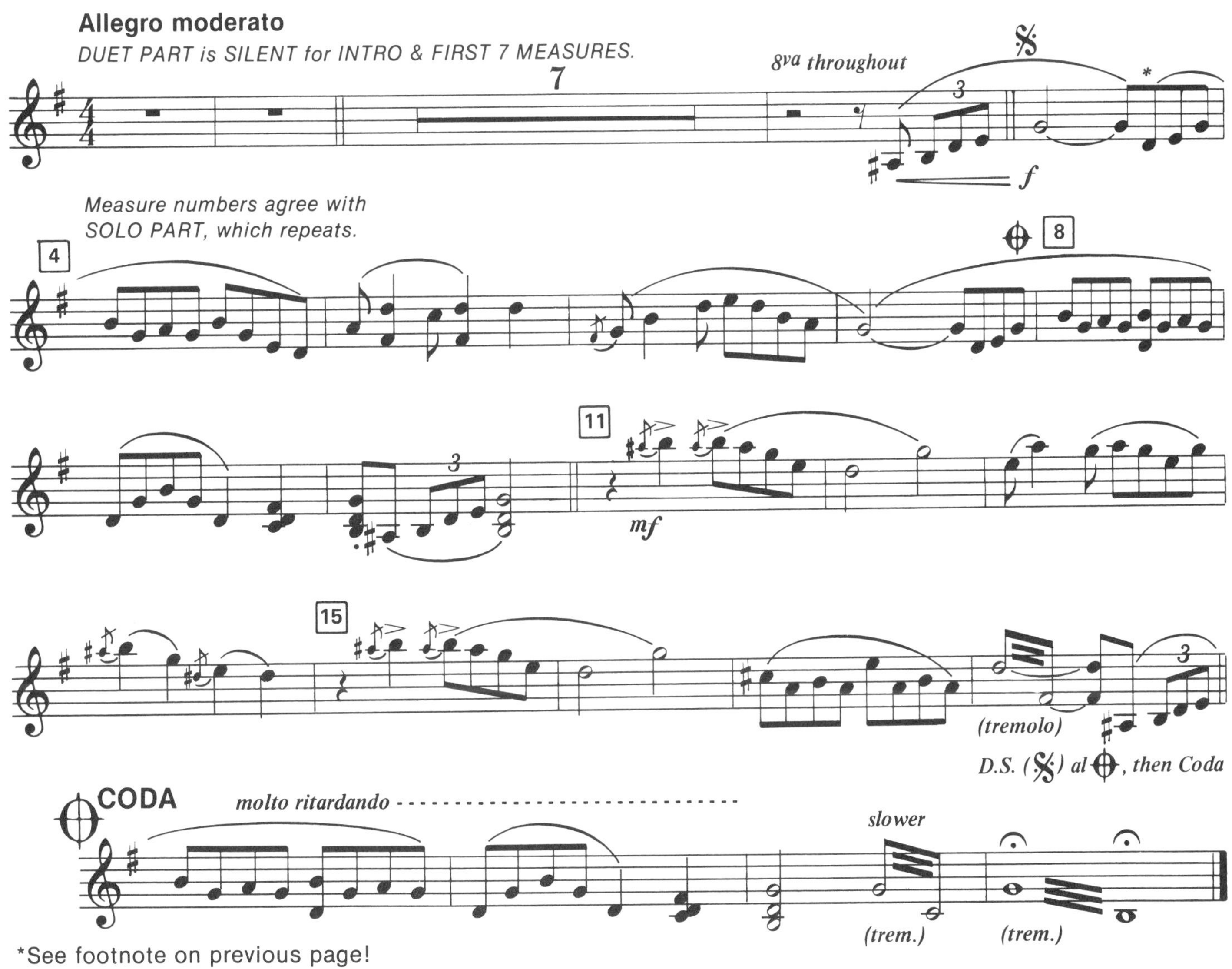

*See footnote on previous page!

Ukrainian Bell Carol

Allegro

M. Leontovich

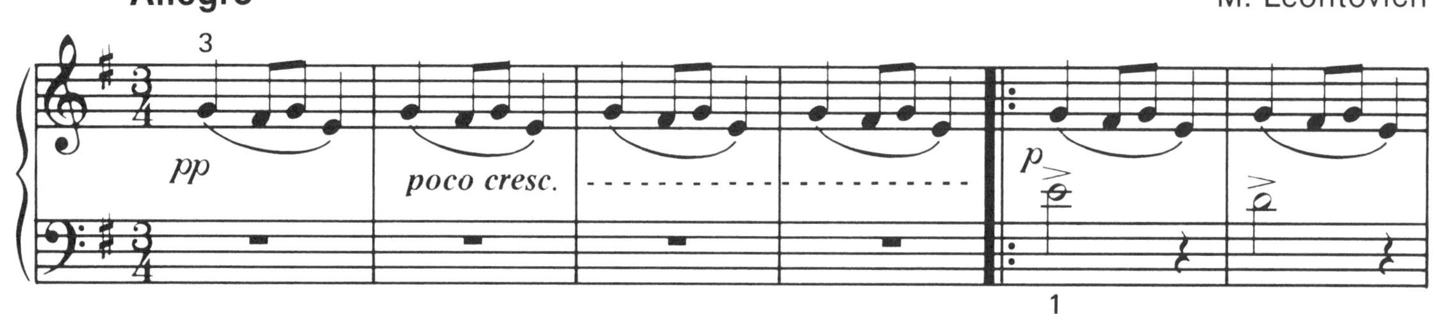

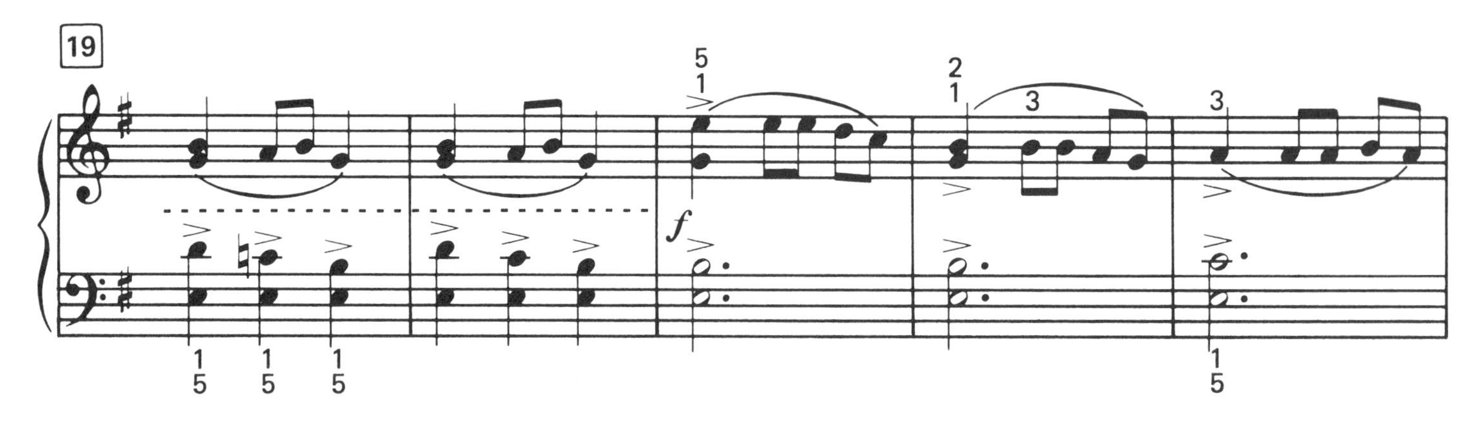

24
29
mf
poco dim.
p
35
1.
2.
Slow
dim.
pp
8va
DUET PART:
Allegro
Play this part 8va throughout.
R.H.
L.H.
7
pp
p
poco cresc.
13
19
mf
poco cresc.
24
f
29
mf
poco dim.
p
35
1.
2.
dim.
pp

O Come, Little Children
Traditional
Andante
O come, lit - tle chil - dren, come one and come all, O
come to the man - ger in Beth - le-hem's stall.
Come see where He li - eth, the heav - en - ly Child,
So poor and so hum - ble, So meek and so mild.
ritard.
DUET PART:
Andante
Play this part 8va throughout.
ritard.